ANIMALS AT HOME

The Penguin

Idea and Illustrations by Iliane Roels

Translated by Marion Koenig

GROSSET & DUNLAP · NEW YORK

Published by Grosset & Dunlap, Inc. 1969

Published in Great Britain and English Translation
© 1968 by W. & R. Chambers Ltd, 11 Thistle Street, Edinburgh 2
©1967 I.C.I. (International Copyright Institute)

Printed in Belgium 1969 by Van den Bossche S.A.

Library of Congress Catalog Card Number: 71-93446

Can you imagine a land where there is nothing but ice and snow? Where no tree or bush grows and where day is dark as night for four months every year? In this land it is as cold in summer as it is during our coldest winters, and in winter it is too icy for us even to imagine.

Yet animals live in this land at the South Pole and penguins spend the greater part of the year there. They prefer to stay in the sea, but they must come on land to lay and hatch their eggs.

The big family of Emperor Penguins arrives every autumn. At first only one or two birds climb ashore. But very soon there is a crowd, first of hundreds then, thousands, standing on the ice.

One day a mother penguin lays her egg. She lays it on the ice for there is nothing in this land with which to build a nest.

But penguins know how to look after their eggs. Skillfully, the father penguin rolls the egg on top of his toes with his beak and squats over it. There is a feather-lined pocket of skin into which the egg fits neatly. There it lies, warm and safe.

For the next two months he must be careful to see that the egg does not fall out.

He stands on the ice, eating nothing except a little snow, until the penguin chick hatches.

Meanwhile the mother penguin has gone off to look for food. It is a long way to the sea, for the bay has frozen over by now. She waddles over ice floes and crevasses, because even though penguins are birds, they cannot fly. In water they are swift and agile, spending all day swimming and diving, to catch fish and crabs.

Life in the sea can be dangerous. Near an ice floe lurks a leopard seal. It darts out suddenly to hunt a penguin but, quick as a flash, the penguin dives and escapes. There is also a killer whale nearby which must be avoided.

After catching enough fish, the mother penguin starts back. The father and their baby eagerly await her. They are both very hungry.

The moment she arrives, the mother takes the baby onto her toes, and feeds fish to it. Now the father goes off to sea.

All over the shore, baby penguins crouch on the toes of their mothers. It is not long before the baby penguins have grown big enough to waddle about on ice and play together. One little penguin is standing all by himself watching them. The others don't like him. They push him away when he tries to play, for he is not gray like them, but white all over.

When the icy blizzard comes, the penguins huddle close together. They lie across each other like the tiles on a roof, each trying to get farther down, away from the wind and snow. Now it is dangerous to be alone. If the little white penguin had not crept into a hole in the ice he would certainly have frozen to death.

Next morning, along comes an enormous bird of prey, called a skua. Flapping its wings, it lands on a block of ice. It is hungry and looking for stray or dead penguins. But no penguin has died during the blizzard, and the little white penguin is not alone any more. He has at last found a friend.

The bird goes on looking for a while longer. The baby penguins duck anxiously when they see the big sharp beak overhead. Then, still hungry, the bird flies out to sea.

Spring has come and the ice in the bay has begun to melt. Soon it is not such a long way to open water. Even the young penguins can manage to reach it. The ice is broken and there are cracks everywhere. Carefully, parents and children waddle down to the sea on their short legs. The young

ones are still a bit timid and even their parents stand, hesitating, on the edge. You can never tell if killer whales or leopard seals are lurking in the ocean depths. Everyone waits for the first penguin to jump, then the rest hop in too. Like arrows they shoot through the water, propelled by their flipper-wings, the little white penguin and his friend leading the way.

By the time summer comes the young ones are big enough to catch their own fish and to swim away with their parents. One by one the penguins leave the land of ice. Nobody knows where they go. But one thing is certain: they will be back in autumn, ready to hatch more eggs when winter comes.